The REINDEER HERDER and the MOON

Bob Barton

Illustrated by Wayne Anderson

BBC/LONGMAN

Moon was lonely.
He had fallen in love
with a young reindeer herder
on the earth beneath,
and he couldn't stop thinking about her.

"Put her out of your mind," warned the stars.
"She belongs on earth:
your place is here in the heavens,
shining along with the rest of us."

But Moon paid no attention.
He dreamed of having the girl by his side.

One night, as he watched her returning
to her camp on the back of a large reindeer,
he was overcome by a powerful urge
to fetch her. Immediately, he started
to climb down.

At first the girl didn't see him.
Then she looked up.
"How close the moon appears!" she said.

She raised her hand to shield her eyes
from his brightness and saw
his long spindly legs and skinny arms.
The sight of him was terrifying.

"Oh!" she cried, "the Moon Man
is coming for me! What can I do?"

Her reindeer turned and spoke.
"Jump from my back. I'll dig a hole
in the snow for you to hide in."

With his powerful hind legs the reindeer
kicked a hollow in the snow. The girl
jumped in and the reindeer pushed snow
all around her, leaving only the top
of her white fur hood uncovered.
Then the reindeer moved into the distance.

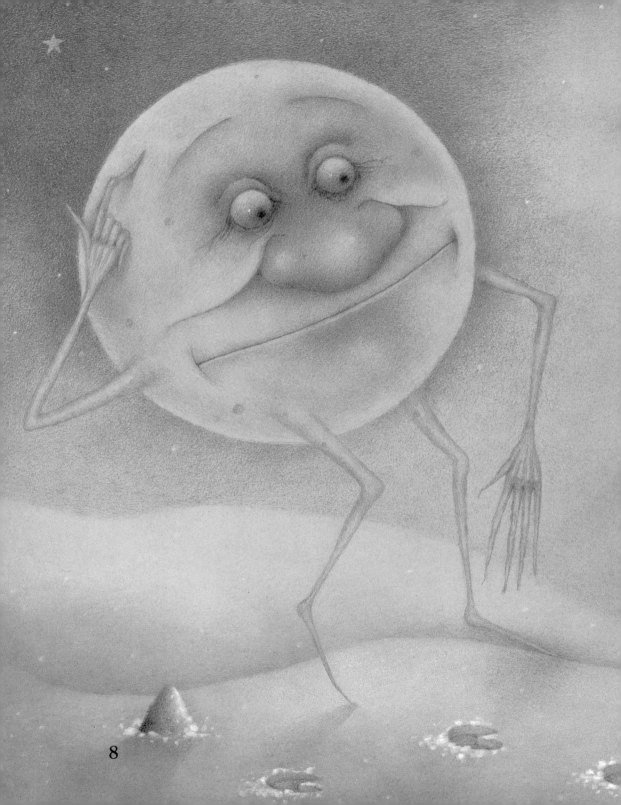

8

Moon stepped on to the earth. His thin legs
moved unsteadily beneath the weight
of his body. He looked from side to side.
He had expected to see the herder
and her reindeer. He had not expected to see
an empty landscape.
"Where is she?" muttered Moon.
"She was here only moments ago."

He was standing practically on top of her
as he spoke. Then he spied tracks
in the snow. He started to follow them,
but soon thought better of the idea.
He wasn't used to walking about like this.

9

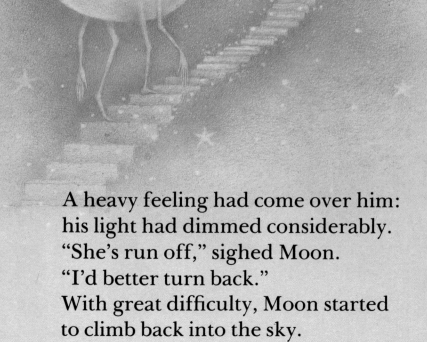

A heavy feeling had come over him:
his light had dimmed considerably.
"She's run off," sighed Moon.
"I'd better turn back."
With great difficulty, Moon started
to climb back into the sky.

The higher he climbed the brighter he became.
The higher he climbed the stronger he felt.
Soon he floated easily among the stars.

11

On earth, the reindeer dug the girl
from the snow. She leapt to his back
and made haste to her camp.
Moon looked down and saw her.
He plunged instantly towards the earth.

The reindeer saw him coming and shouted,
"The Moon is returning!"

"I must hide!" cried the girl. "Where?"

"I can hide you," said the reindeer.
"With my magic powers I can transform you
into something else. You could become
a tent pole."

"No," said the girl. "He might crush the tent."

"You could become one of the skins
on the sleeping platform."

"He could carry that off," replied the girl.

The reindeer looked about hurriedly.
"I have it!" he said. "I can change you
into an oil lamp. In the glare
of Moon's brightness you won't be noticed."

And that's what he did. He struck
his front hoof on the snow three times,
and where the girl had stood
there now appeared a stone oil lamp
burning with a tiny bright flame.
Reindeer hid behind the tent.

14

Moon was picking his way uncertainly
toward the tent. He called to the girl,
reached out, lifted the flap, and peered in.
"Where are you hiding?" demanded Moon.
"Are you under the sleeping platform?"

He raised the sleeping platform.
No one was hiding there.

"Are you behind the tent pole?"

He peeked behind the tent pole.
No one was hiding there.

"Are you under the cooking pot?"

He lifted the cooking pot.
No one was hiding there.

All the time he looked, the tiny lamp flame fluttered and danced in the Arctic night.

Moon withdrew from the tent. He was baffled. "How does she disappear like that?" wondered Moon. "Where does she go?"

There was a giggle from inside the tent.

Moon tore open the tent flap
and barged inside. Nothing had changed.
No one was there. The tiny lamp flame
leapt and whirled in the sudden breeze
Moon had made.

Moon stumbled outside. He didn't feel well.
A great heaviness had come over him
and his light was nearly out.
"The stars were right," thought Moon.
"I've no business being down here."

He was about to leave
when a peal of laughter rang out!

Moon turned. The girl had regained her shape
and was peering at him
from behind the tent flap.
"Here I am!" she taunted.

Moon lurched toward her, stumbled,
and crashed to the snow.

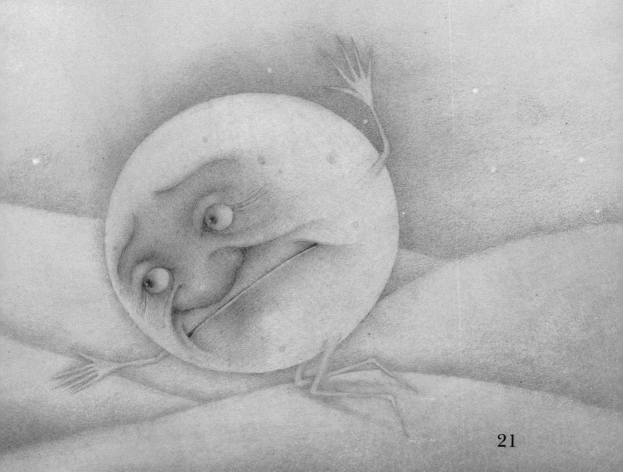

The girl was on him in a flash. She threw
the reindeer harness around his legs,
pulled it tight, and shouted, "So, Moon Man,
it's I who have captured you!"

But Moon said nothing.
His teeth chattered violently. His light
was almost gone. He appeared
completely helpless. When he did speak
his voice came in a whisper.
"Please! Please help me! Unfasten my legs.
Let me return to the skies."

"And if I do, you will grow strong again and come back for me," said the girl.

"No, never!" cried Moon. "I shall never come down from the skies again. Please release me and I will reward you and all your people."

"And what reward would that be, Moon Man?"

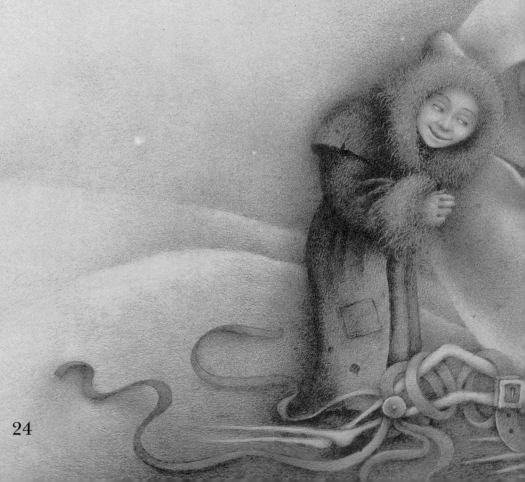

Moon's voice was so weak now that the girl
had to put her ear to his lips.
When he finished speaking, her face beamed.

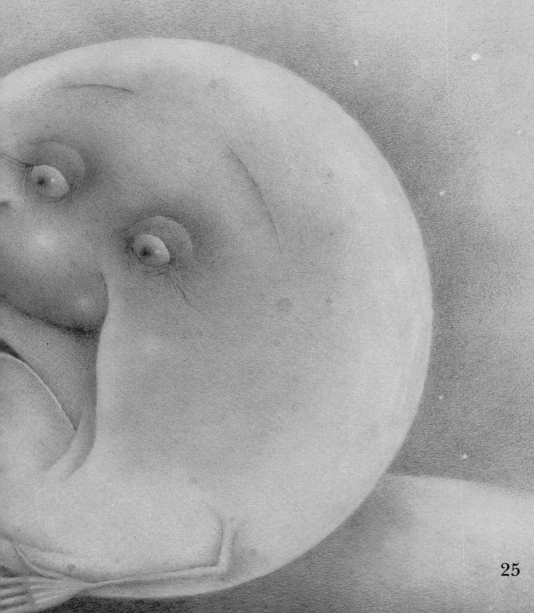

She leapt to her feet, whistled
to her reindeer and freed Moon's legs.
Next, she slipped the harness
under Moon's arms, tossed one end
to the reindeer, who gripped it in his teeth,
and while she pushed from behind
the reindeer pulled.

Moon rose slowly to his feet.
Supported by the girl on one side,
and the reindeer on the other, he took
a few halting steps, then started climbing.

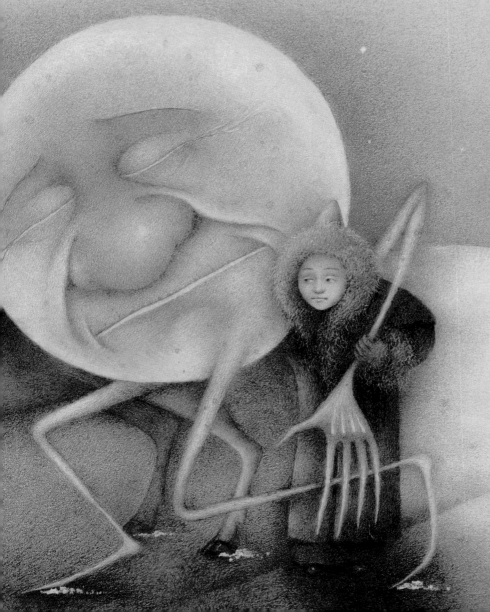

Higher and higher he climbed.
Brighter and brighter he became.
Soon he had regained his rightful place
among the stars.

True to his word, Moon rewarded the girl
and her people. He became
their nightly beacon, guiding them across
their frozen lands. He became their calendar,
measuring the year for them.

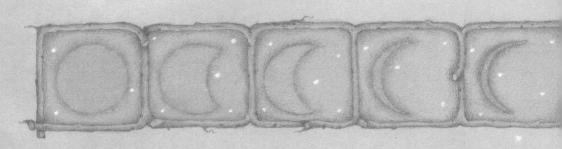

He became for her people
The Moon of the Old Bull
The Moon of the Birth of Calves
The Moon of the Waters.

He became
The Moon of Leaves
The Moon of Warmth
The Moon of the Shedding of Antlers.

He became
The Moon of Love Among the Wild Deer
The Moon of the First Winter
The Moon of the Shortening Days.

And true to his word, he never came down
to earth again.

Other titles in this series

The tiger and the poor man by Beulah Candappa
The Nung-Guama by Roger Lancelyn Green
The green man by Gail Haley
Who's afraid now? by Rose Impey
The days of the banyan tree by Madhur Jaffrey
Miss MacDonald had a zoo by Cecily O'Neill
In the middle of the night by Philippa Pearce
Open wide by Mary Rayner
The nagging husband by James Riordan

Series consultants: Myra Barrs and Sue Ellis, Director and Deputy Director of
the Centre for Learning in Primary Education (Southwark).

The series accompanies the BBC School Radio series, *Listening and Reading* on
Radio 5 Medium Wave.

Published by BBC Educational Publishing and Longman Group UK Limited

BBC Educational Publishing
a division of
BBC Enterprises Limited
Woodlands
80 Wood Lane
London W12 0TT

Longman Group Limited
Longman House
Burnt Mill
Harlow
Essex CM20 2JE
England and associated
companies throughout the world

First published 1990
© BBC Enterprises Limited/Longman Group UK Limited 1990
Text © Bob Barton 1990
Illustrations © Wayne Anderson 1990

Series editor Joan Griffiths
Cover and book design by
Claire Robertson
(school edition) ISBN 0 582 06207 1
(trade edition) ISBN 0 563 34762 7

Set in 16/20pt Baskerville
Typeset by Goodfellow and Egan
Text and cover origination by
Dot Gradations
Printed and bound by Cambus Litho